A Teddy Horsley

Neighbo

Betsy Bear helps her Neighbours

Based on the Great Commandment from Luke 10

by Leslie J Francis and Nicola M Slee
Pictures by Laura Cooper

The Bear facts:

The Teddy Horsley Bible Series is designed to build bridges between the young child's day to day experiences of the world and major biblical themes and stories.

Both authors work in church-linked colleges concerned with Teacher Education. Nicola Slee lectures in Religious Studies at Whitelands College in London. Leslie Francis is Research Fellow at Trinity College in Carmarthen.

The Teddy Horsley Series is a result of both authors' extensive research into the religious development of young children and their wide experience of educational work in schools and churches.

Published by:
National Christian Education Council
Robert Denholm House
Nutfield, Redhill, RH1 4HW, England

British Library Cataloguing-in-Publication Data:
A catalogue record for this book is available from the British Library.

Series editor: David Martin
Text © Leslie J Francis and Nicola M Slee 1990
Illustrations © National Christian Education Council 1994

First published 1990 by Bible Society, England   Reprinted 1994
ISBN 0-7197-0846-X   Printed in England

Betsy Bear likes to meet her neighbours.

She gets up early to see the dustman

and runs down the path to meet the postlady.

She calls to the woman next door hanging out her washing

and waves to the man down the road weeding
his garden.

She watches the people waiting at the bus stop

and chats to her friends riding on the bus.

She plays with the children running in the park

and laughs with the babies sitting in their prams.

She pushes her trolly round the supermarket
and smiles at the shoppers waiting at the checkout.

Whoever she meets in the wide, wide world
Betsy Bear knows they are all her neighbours.

Betsy Bear likes to help her neighbours.

She picks up some waste paper for the dustman.

She opens the garden gate for the postlady

and carries the pegs for the woman hanging out
her washing.

She fetches the water for the man weeding his garden

and looks after a bag for a mother at the bus stop.

She gives up her seat for an old man on the bus

and pushes a girl on the swing at the park.

She cheers up a baby crying in his pushchair.

She unloads her shopping at the checkout
and helps the man pack it in boxes.

Whoever she helps in the wide, wide world,
Betsy Bear knows they are all her neighbours.

The Teddy Horsley Bible Series is designed to build bridges between the young child's day to day experiences of the world and major biblical themes and stories.

In *Neighbours*, Betsy Bear's experience of meeting and helping her neighbours brings alive the Great Commandment of Luke 10:

A teacher of the Law came up and tried to trap Jesus. "Teacher," he asked, "what must I do to receive eternal life?"
Jesus answered him, "What do the Scriptures say? How do you interpret them?"
The man answered, " 'Love the Lord your God with all your heart, with all your soul, with all your strength, and with all your mind'; and 'Love your neighbour as you love yourself.' "
"You are right," Jesus replied; "do this and you will live."
But the teacher of the Law wanted to justify himself, so he asked Jesus, "Who is my neighbour?"

Luke 10. 25-29

The following questions suggest further ways of developing the links between the Bible passage and the young child's experience.

Talk about meeting and helping neighbours:

Who are your neighbours?
When do you meet them?
Where do you meet them?
How do you help them?

Talk about the story:

Who were Betsy Bear's neighbours?
When did she meet them?
Where did she meet them?
How did she help them?

Think some more about the story:

What other neighbours might Betsy Bear meet?
When would she meet them?
Where would she meet them?
How would she help them?

Think about the Bible passage:

Who do you love?
How do you show your love for them?
How do people show love for their neighbours?
How would you answer the teacher's final question to Jesus?

Titles in the series

Other publications to help young children explore the Bible:

Bible Storyboards — Wooden play-tray jigsaws, which present a Bible story in six scenes with ''lift-out'' characters, ''match-up'' pictures, and story-telling script. Designed to encourage learning through play.

Open House Books — Six house-shaped board books focussing on the homes of well known Bible characters. Simple storylines relate Bible stories associated with each place.

Bible Storygraphics — A video giving ten-minute presentations of three well known Bible stories using narration, music, and computer-generated graphics.